Late Night at the Zoo

Written by Mairi Mackinnon

Illustrated by John Joven

How this book works

The story of **Late Night at the Zoo** has been written for your child to read with your help. Encourage your child to read as much as they can, helping to sound out the words if they get stuck.

There are puzzles after the story, and for these you will need to read the instructions to your child.

You can find out more about helping your child with this book, and with reading in general, on pages 30-31.

Late Night at the Zoo

Turn the page to start the story.

It's late at the zoo, and the crowds go back home.

But do you suppose
that we just sit and moan?

Not us! We need no excuse for a tune.

Oh, we do like a sing-song under the moon.

It's late at the zoo, but
these snakes are awake.

"Shall we play a game?
Let us chase, you escape."

It's late at the zoo.
See the big gum trees?

These baboons have
set up a flying trapeze.

It's late at the zoo.
Soon the zebras arrive.

And the pandas are saying,
"It's time for a ride."

And we gallop around,
until we collide.

Then you see,
in the daytime,
we just sleep inside.

Puzzle 1

What is it? Choose the right description for each picture.

1.

A It's a sing-song.

B It's a game of ping-pong.

2.

A It's a game.

B It's a picture frame.

3.

A It's a cooling breeze.

B It's a flying trapeze.

4.

A It's time for a ride.

B It's time for the slide.

Puzzle 2

Choose the right word to complete each phrase.

1.

The crowds go back ....

hole	home	hope

2.

These .... are awake.

stakes

3.

.... the zebras arrive.

Noon	Moon	Soon

4.

We just .... inside.

sheep	sleep	steep

Puzzle 3

The words on the left are all in the story. Can you find their opposites on the right?

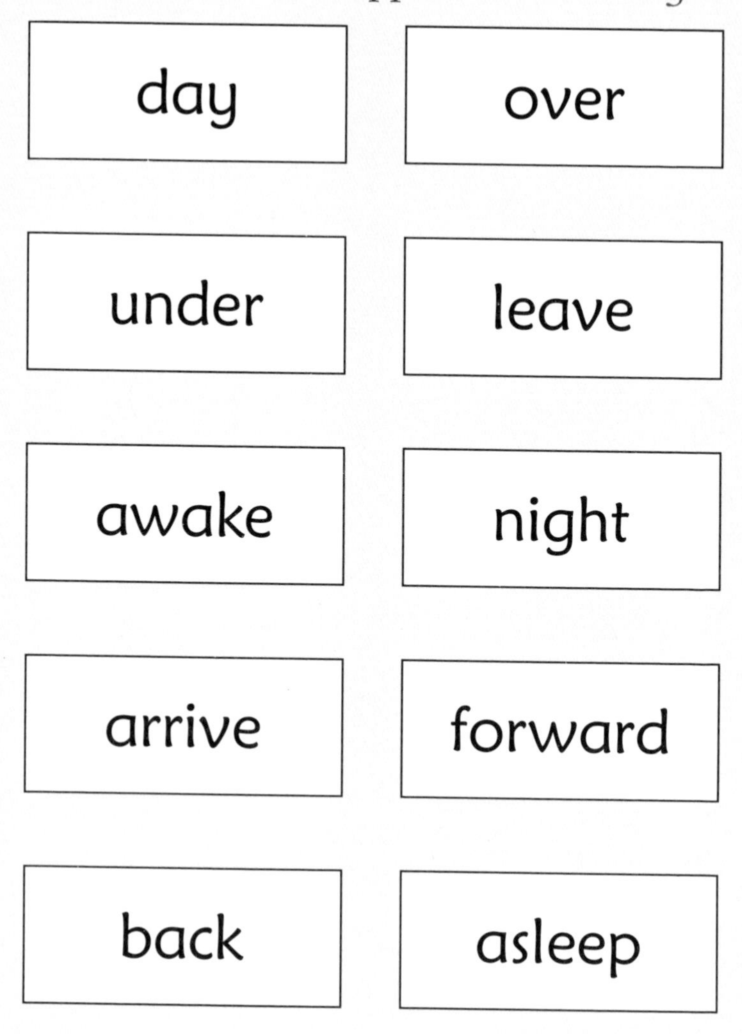

Answers to puzzles

Puzzle 1

1. A It's a sing-song.
2. A It's a game.
3. B It's a flying trapeze.
4. A It's time for a ride.

Puzzle 2

1. The crowds go back <u>home</u>.
2. These <u>snakes</u> are awake.
3. <u>Soon</u> the zebras arrive.
4. We just <u>sleep</u> inside.

Puzzle 3

day → night

under → over

awake → asleep

arrive → leave

back → forward

Guidance notes

Usborne Very First Reading is a series of books, specially developed for children who are learning to read. **Late Night at the Zoo** is the tenth book in the series, and by this stage your child should be able to read the story alone, with occasional help from you.

The story of **Late Night at the Zoo** introduces the following spelling patterns:

a e   e e   i e   o e   u e

These are sometimes referred to as "the magic e" – it can be a tricky concept at first (one letter-sound changes because of another letter later in the word), but words spelled in this way tend to be pronounced very consistently. Later books in the series gradually introduce more spelling patterns, while reinforcing the ones your child already knows.

You'll find lots more information about the structure of the series, advice on helping your child with reading, extra practice activities and games on the Very First Reading website,*
www.usborne.com/veryfirstreading

*US readers go to **www.veryfirstreading.com**

Some questions and answers

- **Why do I need to read with my child?**
  Sharing stories makes reading an enjoyable and fun activity for children. It also helps them to develop confidence and stamina. Even if you are not taking an active part in reading, your listening and support are very important.
- **When is a good time to read?**
  Choose a time when you are both relaxed, but not too tired, and there are no distractions. Only read for as long as your child wants to – you can always try again another day.
- **What if my child gets stuck?**
  Don't simply read the problem word yourself, but prompt your child and try to find the right answer together. Similarly, if your child makes a mistake, go back and look at the word together. Don't forget to give plenty of praise and encouragement.
- **We've finished, now what do we do?**
  It's a good idea to read the story several times to give your child more practice and more confidence. Then, when your child is ready, you can go on to the next book in the series, **Wild School.**

Edited by Jenny Tyler and Lesley Sims
Designed by Caroline Spatz

This edition first published in 2013 by Usborne Publishing Ltd., Usborne House, 83-85 Saffron Hill, London EC1N 8RT, England. www.usborne.com
UE. First published in America in 2010.